Welcome to the

SPIDER-MAN

ANNUAL 2007

INSIDE...

SPIDER-FILE 1: ORIGINS — 4
Top-secret data on the making of a Super-Hero!

ADVENTURE STORY: MARKED FOR DESTRUCTION BY DR. DOOM! — 6
Spidey takes on Dr. Doom and an army of Doombots!

SPIDER-FILE 2: DR. DOOM — 12
Everything you were too afraid to ask about the deranged doc!

SPIDER-FILE 3: DR. DOOM'S LATVERIAN EMBASSY — 20
An access-all-areas tour through the lair of a lunatic!

PUZZLES: BATTLE ZONE — 34
Go head-to-head with some of the world's deadliest villains!

ADVENTURE STORY: THE GROTESQUE ADVENTURE OF THE GREEN GOBLIN! — 36
The Goblin lures Spidey into a deadly trap!

SPIDER-FILE 4: GREEN GOBLIN — 42
Discover the twisted truth about the masked maniac!

SPIDER-FILE 5: MOST WANTED — 52
Meet Spidey's five most dangerous enemies... IF YOU DARE!

PUZZLES: PATH OF DESTINY — 62
Hero or villain – it's time to choose your destiny!

D0349521

£6.99

ORIGINS

> WELCOME, TRUE BELIEVER ....
> YOU ARE ACCESSING THE SPIDER FILES ....
> YOU HAVE CHOSEN SPIDER FILE 1: ORIGINS ....

> WARNING: THIS FILE CONTAINS TOP-SECRET DATA
ON THE HISTORY OF SPIDER-MAN, SO KEEP IT SAFE ....

THE BEGINNING...

Before he became Spider-Man, Peter Parker was just an ordinary kid who lived with his aunt and uncle in a small house in Forest Hills, New York. Ever since his parents died Peter had found it difficult to make friends, and spent most of his time alone, studying his favourite subject – science. But one fateful day, during a school science trip, Peter was bitten by a radioactive spider, and his life changed forever...

DATA FILE> DNA STRANDING: HUMAN/SPIDER...

HUMAN DNA

RADIATION

DANGER! DANGER!
DNA MUTATION

ARACHNID DNA

THE HUMAN SPIDER...

*What happened next is still something of a mystery. Peter's own theory is that when the spider bit him, the massive dose of radiation delivered in the bite caused his DNA to fuse with the spider's DNA, leaving him part man, part spider. But whatever the explanation, it wasn't long before Peter discovered the great gifts, and the great curse, of being a **spider man**...*

DATA FILE> PETER PARKER

POWER...

At first, Peter loved his new spider-like powers. He could stick to walls and leap between buildings, and his strength, speed and agility had grown to super-human levels! Realising his powers could earn him good money as an amateur wrestler, Peter set out for fame and fortune using a makeshift disguise and the stage name, Spider-Man...

RESPONSIBILITY...

*As Peter was leaving the stadium one night, a burglar sped past him. Peter could have stopped him but chose not to, thinking it wasn't his problem. But later that night, his uncle was murdered by the same burglar he had let escape earlier! Peter was traumatised, blaming himself for failing to use his powers when they were **really** needed.*

BIRTH OF A SUPER-HERO...

*But it was in this moment of tragedy that Peter Parker **truly** became a Super-Hero, as he realised that with great power, there must also come great **responsibility**. From that day on, he promised to always use his powers to uphold justice and protect the innocent. And so, after perfecting the disguise and webbing equipment he'd made for his wrestling career, the amazing Spider-Man was born!*

DATA FILE> WEB SHOOTER: DESIGN...

WEB SHOOTERS...

WEB-FLUID CARTRIDGE

TRIGGER - DOUBLE TAP TO FIRE

UTILITY BELT...

SPARE WEB-FLUID CARTRIDGES

SPIDER SIGNAL LAMP

CONTINUED ON PAGE 14...

11

DR. DOOM

> **REAL NAME:** VICTOR VON DOOM ....
> **OCCUPATION:** CRIMINAL MASTERMIND, KING OF LATVERIA ....
> **BASE OF OPERATIONS:** NEW YORK, USA AND LATVERIA, EUROPE ....
> **GOALS:** WORLD DOMINATION, DESTROYING THE FANTASTIC FOUR ....
> **POWERS:** SUPER-STRONG ARMOUR, MAGIC, ENERGY BLASTS ....

INTELLIGENCE	10
STRENGTH	7
ENDURANCE	7
FIGHTING SKILLS	6
DANGER RATING	9

CRIMINAL PROFILE...

Dr. Doom is one of the most dangerous and twisted super-villains on the planet. Hell-bent on world domination and the destruction of Reed Richards and the Fantastic Four, his monstrous rage only increases as his goals continue to evade him. He's become so consumed by these two desires, he barely even remembers the man he once was – the man behind the mask...

Image: Statue of Doom...
Location: Castle Doom, Latveria...

ORIGINS...

Born into the cruel kingdom of Latveria and tormented by the early loss of his parents, child-genius Victor Von Doom was **doomed** from the start. As his hatred of the world grew, so did his mastery of science and the art of dark magic. After years abroad developing his powers and twisted inventions, Victor returned to Latveria and brutally conquered it. On that day, the whole world learned to fear the name Victor Von Doom!

ARMOUR...

Doom's armour is the source of many of his powers, including super-human strength, forcefield generation, and the ability to fire energy blasts from his hands. But such power came at a terrible price, for when the suit was made, Doom wore the mask before the metal had cooled, scarring his face horribly. He now rarely removes it, dreading the sight of his own reflection.

DOOMBOTS...

When Dr. Doom invented the Doombots, it was probably his vanity that urged him to make them exact copies of himself. But over the years, having robotic clones of himself has proved very handy, helping him confuse and defeat many enemies. Until recently, the workings of a Doombot have been a total mystery. But now, thanks to Spidey capturing this damaged model, the Doombot's secrets can finally be told!

NANO COMPUTER

Using the most advanced computer chip in the world, the bot's A.I. programming is SO detailed, they actually believe they're the real, human Dr. Doom!

SELF-DESTRUCTOR

A recent addition, allowing Doom to remote detonate a bot should it step out of line.

PISTOL

The 9mm Broom-Handle Mauser pistol is, by today's standards, an antique. Though it still packs a deadly punch, it's worn more as a mark of status – something very common with the Latverian ruling classes.

ARMOUR

Believing **themselves** to be the true Dr. Doom, many bots have tried to destroy their master. So to protect himself, Doom deliberately made the Doombots' armour weaker than his own.

VOICE BOX

Developed to mimic the real Doom's voice, helping to fool enemies.

BEAM BLASTERS

Fires high-energy particle beams capable of melting titanium.

SHIELD GENERATOR

Projects a force-field around the bot capable of withstanding a force 9 energy blast. When activated, the shield will also deliver a 30,000 volt shock to anyone who touches it.

DATA FILE>
DOOMBOT
DESIGN...

13..

Forest Hills, Queens.

HEY, LOOK AT ME! I'M SPIDER-MAN!

BOY, PETER PARKER'S GOING TO FREAK OUT WHEN HE SEES YOU, FLASH!

YEAH, TEN BUCKS SAYS HE TELLS SPIDEY HE'S HIS BIGGEST FAN.

YOU THINK HE'LL FALL FOR IT, LIZ?

YOU BET!

WELL, THANKS FOR MAKING THIS FOR ME, GIRLS. PUNY PARKER'S GONNA GET THE SURPRISE OF HIS LIFE!

Latverian Embassy.

DIDN'T TAKE MUCH FOR SOMEONE WITH MY INTELLIGENCE TO REVERSE THE EFFECTS OF THIS COMMUNICATION DEVICE. WITH THESE NEW MODIFICATIONS, I HAVE NOW DISCOVERED A WAY TO TRACK SPIDER-MAN.

WHEN ONE IS A MASTER OF SCIENCE, AS I AM, THERE IS NOTHING THAT CANNOT BE ACCOMPLISHED!

SOON, ALL WHO OPPOSE ME WILL BE ELIMINATED!

THERE'S PETER PARKER.

OK, FLASH, HE'S COMING. GET READY!

CONTINUED ON PAGE 24... **19**...

DR. DOOM'S LATVERIAN EMBASSY

OPTICAL ZOOM>X2000

M1/2000 F5.6

[230]

OPTICAL ZOOM>X2000

> OPENING SPIDER FILE 3 ....
> YOU ARE ABOUT TO ENTER ONE OF THE WORLD'S
  MOST SECRET BUILDINGS .... WARNING: YOU MAY
  FIND SOME DATA DISTURBING ....

DATA FILE> LATVERIAN EMBASSY> SKY LEVEL...

SKY LEVEL

GROUND LEVEL

SUB LEVEL

SITE: LATVERIAN EMBASSY

OWNER: VICTOR VON DOOM

LOCATION: NEW YORK, USA

FUNCTION: CRIMINAL HEADQUARTERS

SECURITY: HIGH – MOTION SENSING
CAMERAS, AUTO-GUNS,
LASER GRIDS, DOOMBOTS

The Latverian Embassy is the official New York
residence of criminal mastermind and Latverian
ruler, VICTOR VON DOOM. To the outside world, it's
just a regular, boring government building from
where Doom looks after the foreign affairs of his
home country, LATVERIA. But thanks to Spidey and
his hidden camera, the Embassy's sinister secrets
and terrible truths have finally been revealed...

SKY LEVEL

SPACE OBSERVATORY

Equipped with a neutron telescope and inter-stellar monitoring gear for tracking the Fantastic Four's spacecraft and selecting targets for the Doom Ray.

DESK OF DOOM

This is where Doom draws up his despicable plans. The desk's built-in targeting computer is linked to his Doom Ray, giving him the power to wipe out planet-sized targets at the touch of a button!

DOOM RAY

One of Doom's most terrifying inventions, the Doom Ray is capable of vaporizing entire planets! Though he's never actually fired it, Doom often uses the ray to threaten alien civilisations into his service.

HELI-PAD

To avoid detection from above, the heli-pad is raised and lowered by a hydraulic lift. The helicopter's rotor blades fold to allow it to fit into the secret hanger.

NANO GLASS

To prevent the outside world spying on Doom's secret activities, the windows project a false vision of the interior, giving the impression of a normal embassy building hiding inside.

GUEST ROOMS

The guest rooms are bugged and fitted with surveillance cameras, allowing Doom to spy on foreign leaders and officials staying at the embassy.

SECRET DOORS

As the Ruler of Latveria, Doom often has government officials and ambassadors visiting his embassy. To ensure his evil operations are not discovered, the building's secret rooms can only be accessed through hidden doors concealed behind bookshelves, paintings and fake walls.

GROUND LEVEL

FUNCTION ROOMS

Where Doom addresses and entertains foreign leaders foolish enough to trust him. Both the Grand Ballroom and the Banqueting Hall are bugged and booby-trapped.

INVENTING LAB

The birthplace of some of Dr Doom's most startling creations. Under his orders, a specialised team of Doombots work 24 hours a day researching and constructing his latest inventions.

DOOM CHAIRS

If any guest dares to oppose Doom's will, their chair instantly drops into the underground dungeon, from where few people return.

SPY ROOMS

Secret rooms accessible only through hidden doors. From here, Doom's servants can monitor every inch of the embassy. Useful for spying on visiting officials and Doom's OWN servants to ensure they remain loyal!

TIME MACHINE

Of all Doom's inventions, his time machine has to be the greatest. This, his latest model, works by creating a wormhole in space through which he can travel to any time and place in the history of the galaxy!

DOOM'S OFFICE

Where he holds private meetings with diplomats and visiting leaders, hoping to intimidate them into forming political and military allegiances with Latveria.

SUB LEVEL

ESCAPE TUNNEL

In case of emergency, Doom can make a speedy exit through this secret underground tunnel.

COLD FUSION GENERATOR

Doom is the only scientist to have successfully stabilised a cold fusion energy generator. Without it, Doom would not have enough power to fuel all his experiments and inventions.

GRAVITY LIFT

A zero-gravity lift shaft that allows Doom and his servants to literally float from one floor to the next!

TRAP DOOR

A deadly security device to deal with unwanted guests like Spider-Man.

When the victim is in place, the floor slides away, dropping them into a lethal propeller shaft!

DOOMBOT FACTORY

A small-scale assembly line building replacement bots for those destroyed during battles with the Fantastic Four and Spider-Man.

DUNGEON

A cruel and hopeless place where prisoners and victims of the Doom Chairs are caged, tortured and terminated.

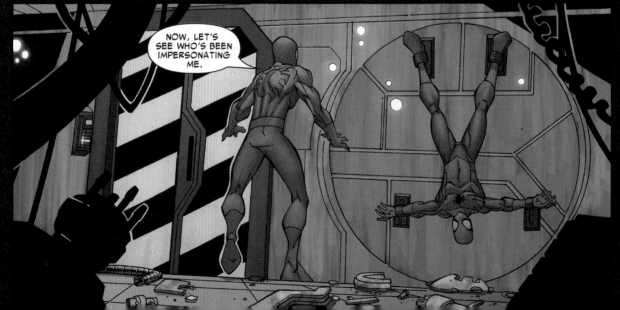

BEN, HONEY, PUT THE BOY DOWN. HE'S JUST A SCARED LITTLE KID.

YEAH, I DOUBT HE'LL BE IMPERSONATING ANYMORE SUPER HEROES ANYTIME SOON.

AUNT MAY?! ARE YOU HERE?

IS THAT YOU, PETER? WHAT TOOK YOU SO LONG? DO YOU HAVE THE FUSES?

UM, NO, I UH, I SAW SOME PRETTY TOUGH-LOOKING GUYS ON THE STREET AND HAD TO LAY LOW UNTIL THEY LEFT. BY THEN IT WAS TOO LATE TO GO TO THE STORE. SORRY.

OH, DON'T WORRY ABOUT THAT, DEAR... HAVE YOU EVER CONSIDERED ENROLLING IN A SELF-DEFENSE CLASS?

The Next Day...

Wonder what this is all about.

THAT'S WHEN I SLIPPED OUT OF THE SHACKLES AND SURPRISED DR. DOOM FROM BEHIND. HE NEVER KNEW WHAT HIT HIM! I GOT AWAY BEFORE HE EVER REALIZED WHAT HAPPENED!

WEREN'T YOU SCARED AT ALL?

NAH! IN A SITUATION LIKE THAT, ADRENALINE JUST TAKES OVER. NO TIME TO BE SCARED.

HEY, PETER, YOU SHOULD LISTEN TO FLASH'S STORY. HE'S SO BRAVE!

BRAVE, HUH? ARE YOU SURE THAT'S THE REAL FLASH THOMPSON?

End.

BATTLE ZONE

> WELCOME TO THE BATTLE ZONE ....
> THIS COMBAT PROGRAM WILL TEST YOU AGAINST SOME OF SPIDER-MAN'S FIERCEST ENEMIES ....
> YOUR OBJECTIVE: COMPLETE ALL CHALLENGES ....

1. GREEN GOBLIN...

The insane Goblin loves to lure Spidey into deadly games. This time, he's left a poison time-bomb in central New York, and has challenged Spidey to find the abort password! Can you help?

Ready to *play*, Spider-Fool? Here are your instructions:
1. Cross out all the letters that appear TWICE in the grid.
2. Rearrange the left-over letters to find the password.
3. Enter your password into the data-pad to stop the bomb.

L A Z D H X
F K N R D Z
E A H O C E
Y B R P P Y
C X I K G F

☐ ☐ ☐ ☐ ☐ ☐

2. BLACK CAT...

The Black Cat is the world's greatest cat burglar. Amazingly skilled at hiding, sometimes the hardest part of fighting her is **finding** her! Can you spot her in each of these crime photos?

3. DR. DOOM...

When fighting Doc Doom you're never quite sure if it's **really** him, or one of his Doombots! Can you spot the REAL Doom by finding the only one that matches the original?

A

B

C

D

E

F

ORIGINAL...

DATA FILE> BATTLE ZONE: OPEN...
SPIDERMAN ANNUAL 2007

4. CARNAGE...

Carnage is probably the nastiest, most deadly lifeform in existence. If you ever meet him, our advice is this: RUN! Can you lose him by completing this city maze?

START

FINISH

BITTEN BY AN IRRADIATED SPIDER, WHICH GRANTED HIM INCREDIBLE ABILITIES, **PETER PARKER** LEARNED THE ALL-IMPORTANT LESSON, THAT WITH GREAT POWER THERE MUST ALSO COME GREAT RESPONSIBILITY. AND SO HE BECAME THE AMAZING SPIDER-MAN IN

THE GROTESQUE ADVENTURE OF THE GREEN GOBLIN!

Stan Lee & Steve Ditko	Mike Raicht	Shane Davis	Lary Stucker	Udon's Larry Molinar	Dave Sharpe
PLOT	WRITER	PENCILS	INKS	COLORS	LETTERER
MacKenzie Cadenhead & John Barber		C.B. Cebulski	Ralph Macchio	Joe Quesada	Dan Buckley
ASSISTANT EDITORS		EDITOR	CONSULTING EDITOR	EDITOR-IN-CHIEF	PUBLISHER

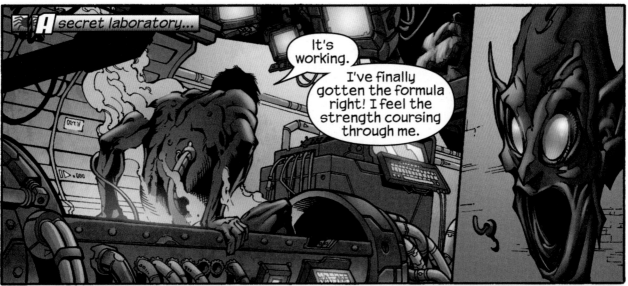

A secret laboratory...

It's working.

I've finally gotten the formula right! I feel the strength coursing through me.

And now with my inventions and newfound super-strength, the world will know--

--that the Green Goblin has arrived!

A motel room nearby...

Why are we here? We don't even know who this Green Goblin guy is...

Chill out, Montana.

The guy is paying us to be here. We're in a penthouse suite!

You should be happy we're getting cash for nothin'.

RRRIIPPP!

NEW

N OK

Well, if he doesn't get here soon I'm gonna do this to him, Dan.

Ox, come on man...what am I doing here with you guys?

I'm sorry to keep you waiting, Enforcers. I know your time is expensive but I have plenty of money so I'm sure you won't mind.

I've got a plan--

Hold up! We've followed the leader before and it didn't work out.

This is my gang now and we're not taking orders from a freak like you.

We'll take your money but we do the job OUR way.

CHIP

OOFFF

CONTINUED ON PAGE 44...

GREEN GOBLIN

> **REAL NAME:** NORMAN OSBORN ....
> **OCCUPATION:** CRIMINAL MASTERMIND, BUSINESSMAN ....
> **BASE OF OPERATIONS:** NEW YORK, USA – EXACT LOCATION UNKNOWN ....
> **GOALS:** KILLING SPIDER-MAN, RULING THE NEW YORK UNDERWORLD ....
> **POWERS:** SUPER-HUMAN STRENGTH, SELF-HEALING ABILITY ....

INTELLIGENCE	7
STRENGTH	7
ENDURANCE	7
FIGHTING SKILLS	6
DANGER RATING	8

CRIMINAL PROFILE...

*Consumed by madness, armed with mind-altering explosives and boosted by a strength-enhancing formula, the Green Goblin has long been Spider-Man's deadliest enemy. His greed for power is matched only by his obsessive hatred of Spider-Man – a mania which has often come close to destroying them both. Like his nemesis, the Goblin keeps his true identity a secret. Of those that **have** discovered it, few have lived to tell the tale...*

ORIGINS...

Ruthless businessman, Norman Osborn, was once head of a major chemical company. But despite already being rich and powerful, Norman wanted more. So he attempted to use an untested strength-boosting serum on himself. The formula exploded in his face, increasing his strength and intelligence, but turning him criminally insane. It was in his madness that he created the freakish identity of the Green Goblin.

POWERS...

The Goblin's powers have grown over the years, as he's continued to improve his Goblin serum. He now has super-human strength and speed, and a greatly accelerated healing ability. In addition, he wears an armoured costume giving him the power to fire electro-beams from his gloves.

OBSESSION...

The Goblin's obsession with Spider-Man is almost as old as the Goblin himself. After creating his new identity, he began plotting to become leader of New York's criminal underworld. Thinking it would earn him a reputation, the Goblin set out to kill Spider-Man. But angered by a string of failed attempts on the web-slinger's life, the Goblin would eventually become **more** concerned with killing Spidey than the reason he targeted him to start with!

EQUIPMENT...

The more desperate the Goblin grew to destroy Spider-Man, the more twisted his arsenal of weapons became. But of all his insane inventions, none strike more fear into the hearts of his enemies than the lightning-fast Goblin Glider and the lethal Pumpkin Bombs...

GOBLIN GLIDER...

FRONT

FOOT STRAPS

AERO-DYNAMIC BAT SHAPE

TOP

JET ENGINE

TOP SPEED: 322 MPH

PUMPKIN BOMBS...

FUSE

POISONOUS VAPOUR

CORE TEMPERATURE: 637^{0}C

DATA FILE: GREEN GOBLIN: GADGETS.

You won't regret this, Spider-Man. We are going to be richer than you could ever imagine! I'll see you in California.

See you there, B.J.!

The Daily Bugle...

So, you're on Spring Break, huh, Peter?

What are you going to do?

Well, actually, Betty, I think I'm going...

Parker! Just the man I wanted to see.

I've got a scoop for you.

Uh--hey, Mr. Jameson. You scared me.

Actually, sir, I've got a trip planned to California and--

That's perfect! I've got a lead that says Spider-Man is going to try to parlay his crime activities into a movie career.

And since you'll already be there, I won't have to pay for room and board. Now get going!

Sure thing, sir.

Be careful out there, Peter. Hollywood is crazier than New York.

46

But Aunt May, it's a chance for me to make some real money taking photos on the set. Mr. Jameson even said he'd pay for the expenses.

Oh, I don't know, Peter. It seems like quite a trip for someone your age.

Aunt May, I would never let you down. You have to trust me. It could get us way ahead.

Will this make you happy, Peter? Do you think some time away doing this will cheer you up?

Yeah, I do.

You're always so serious...okay, you can go.

Thanks, Aunt May!

You're welcome. Just please, be careful.

47...

CONTINUED ON PAGE 54...

51...

MOST WANTED

> OPENING SPIDER FILE 5 .... SUBJECT: SPIDER-MAN'S FIVE DEADLIEST ENEMIES ....
> WARNING: THESE MEN ARE HIGHLY DANGEROUS, SO DO NOT APPROACH ....

INTELLIGENCE	2
STRENGTH	9
ENDURANCE	8
FIGHTING SKILLS	4
DANGER RATING	6

Strong enough to charge through any substance *except lead*, but stupid enough to keep on trying anyway, the Rhino's more **muscle** than **mastermind**. Once just a regular thug in the Russian Mafia, Rhino's natural strength was boosted to super-human levels when an experimental suit of armour was grafted to his body.

5.

RHINO...

POWERS: SUPER-TOUGH ARMOURED SUIT
STRENGTH LEVEL: CAN LIFT OVER 80 TONS

INTELLIGENCE	4
STRENGTH	8
ENDURANCE	8
FIGHTING SKILLS	7
DANGER RATING	7

4.

SANDMAN...

POWERS: ABLE TO TRANSFORM BODY INTO SAND-LIKE FORM
STRENGTH LEVEL: CAN LIFT OVER 85 TONS

Able to change his body into any shape, from rock-hard weapons to intangible sandstorms, the Sandman is one **slippery** customer. After a bizarre nuclear testing accident gave him the power to transform into a sand-like form, the Sandman's become one of the most feared villains in New York.

3.

INTELLIGENCE	8
STRENGTH	5
ENDURANCE	5
FIGHTING SKILLS	6
DANGER RATING	8

DR. OCTOPUS...

POWERS: *FOUR SUPER-STRONG TITANIUM TENTACLES*
STRENGTH LEVEL: *CAN LIFT OVER 10 TONS*

His four deadly, mentally-controlled tentacles, and a ruthless thirst for wealth and power make Dr. Octopus one of the most armed-and-dangerous criminals alive. Formerly a brilliant and good-natured scientist, a tragic accident in the lab left the doc permanently fused to his experimental tentacles, not to mention criminally insane.

2.

VENOM...

POWERS: *SUPER-HUMAN STRENGTH AND AGILITY*
STRENGTH LEVEL: *CAN LIFT OVER 50 TONS*

INTELLIGENCE	5
STRENGTH	7
ENDURANCE	8
FIGHTING SKILLS	9
DANGER RATING	9

As tough and agile as Spider-Man but driven only by hate, Venom is perhaps the web-slinger's ultimate nemesis. He was created when an evil alien parasite took over the body of a lost but good-hearted man, who was just in the wrong place at the wrong time. With teeth and claws as ferocious as his will to survive, there is no living creature more feared than Venom. Except one...

1.

INTELLIGENCE	4
STRENGTH	7
ENDURANCE	7
FIGHTING SKILLS	10
DANGER RATING	10

*A brutal, blood-thirsty killing machine, **Carnage** is quite literally a **monster of a man**. Formed when a pool of Venom's evil alien slime joined together with a psychotic serial killer, he's every bit as powerful as Venom, but a whole lot less friendly. Shortly after his creation, Carnage tore through New York on a rampage so barbaric, Venom himself had to team up with Spider-Man to stop him. Few others who've fought him since have survived, for nothing stands between Carnage and his prey.*

CARNAGE

POWERS: *SUPER-HUMAN STRENGTH AND AGILITY*
STRENGTH LEVEL: *CAN LIFT OVER 50 TONS*

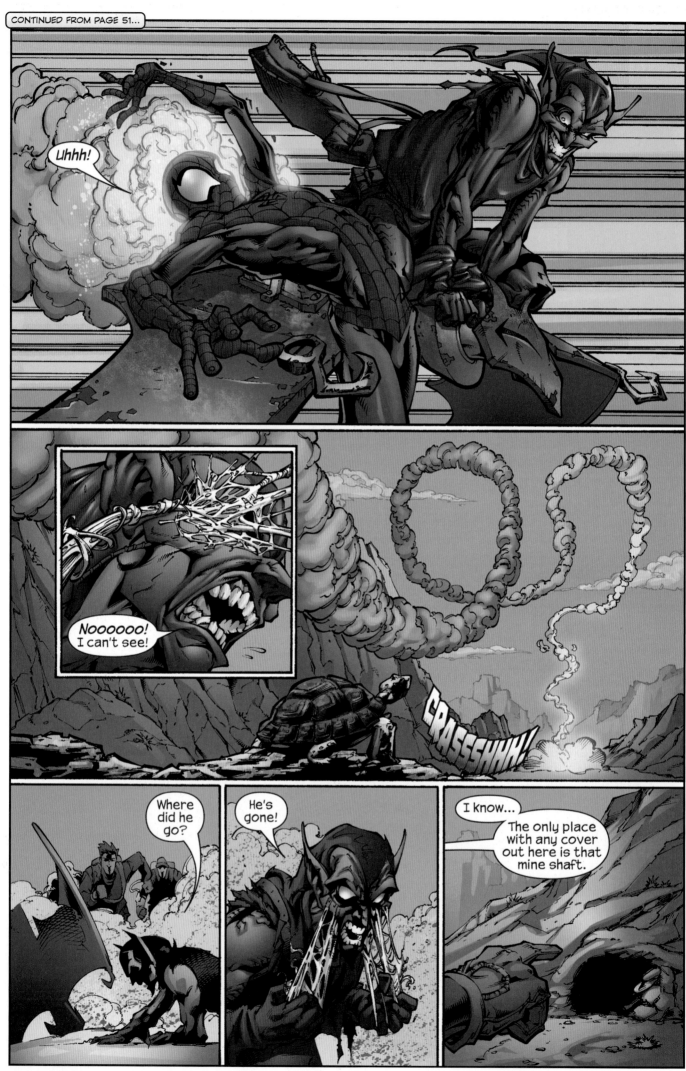

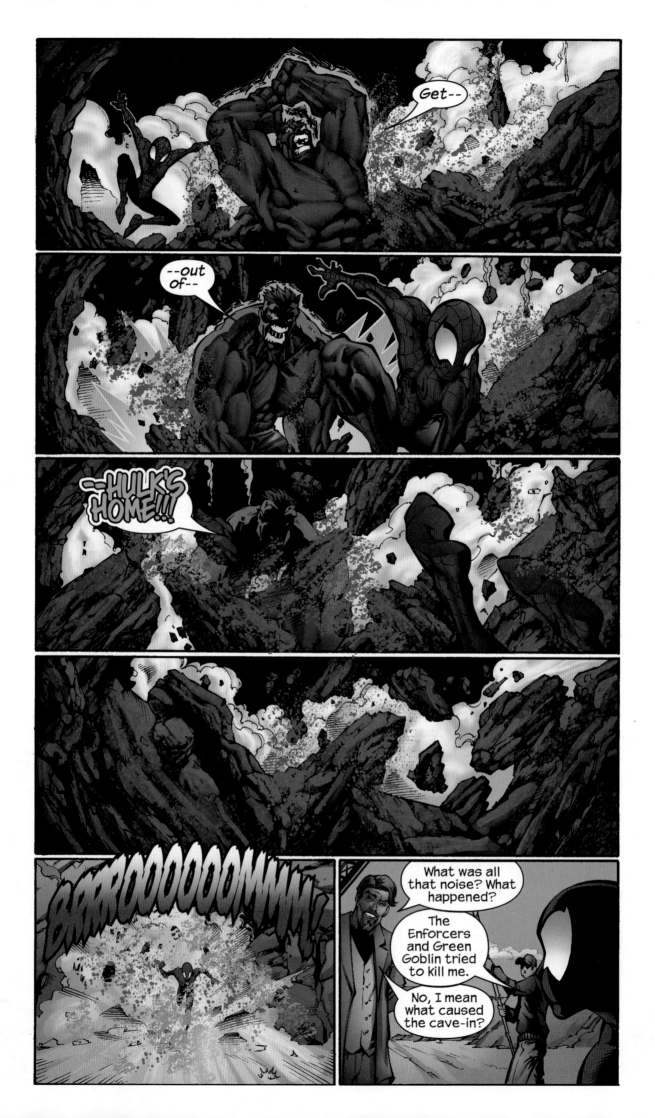

The Hulk is in there and--

The Hulk? Do you know how much money a Hulk movie could fetch me?

A Hulk movie?

But what about the Spider-Man movie? I signed a contract.

A contract that is void if we don't finish the shoot. Which we won't be able to without the rest of the cast.

Read the fine print. And always bring a lawyer, kid.

For your expenses and a bus ride home.

All right, gang, let's get some digging equipment and try to get some Hulk footage.

You've got to be kidding...

A mile away at the other end of the mine shaft...

This is not the last you'll see of me, Spider-Man!

HAHAHAHHAH!

"No, Mr. Jameson. I didn't get any pictures."

Later...

What?! I heard the Hulk was there! And some new costumed freak called the Green Goblin!

My bus is here--I've got to go.

Maybe they're all in cahoots together! Spider-Man...the Hulk... the Green Goblin!

If only I had some pictures of them working together, Parker!

...Parker?

Parker?

End.

PATH OF DESTINY

> OPENING FINAL CHAPTER: PATH OF DESTINY ....
> THIS TEST WILL TELL YOU WHICH PATH YOU ARE
  ON - THE PATH OF THE HERO, OR THE VILLAIN ....
> GOOD LUCK .... YOUR DESTINY AWAITS ....

START

Downtown New York, and the Rhino's playing frisbee with the rush-hour traffic. The city needs your help, but you could get hurt. What do you do?

WAIT FOR HELP

CHASE RHINO

After waiting for five minutes, no help comes. Do you overcome your fear and go after Rhino, or go home for a nice cup of tea, having forgotten what you were waiting for anyway?

CHASE RHINO

Turns out the Rhino's just pulled-off a bank job, and he offers you half the money to help him escape. What do you do?

GO HOME

TAKE THE MONEY AND HELP RHINO

EAT THE MONEY AND FIGHT RHINO

PRETEND TO TAKE THE MONEY THEN CATCH HIM BY SURPRISE

Escaping with your money, a charity worker asks for a donation. Maybe you feel guilty and decide to help, but wouldn't it be funny to burn the money and laugh in their face?

SAY YES

With Rhino caught, a reporter offers to write a heroic story about you. Do you say 'no' - you're not in it for the fame, or 'yes' - it's about time you got some good press!

BURN THE MONEY

DONATE THE MONEY

SAY NO

GREEN GOBLIN

An evil, twisted lunatic, you enjoy causing misery and destruction. You're no better than the Green Goblin!

BLACK CAT

Though you don't always do the right thing, you're not all bad. You are most like the Black Cat.

AUNT MAY

Like Aunt May, you prefer a quiet life, and haven't got time for all this super-hero nonsense.

HULK

You caught Rhino, but destroyed half the city in the process. You, like the Hulk, are brave but reckless.

SPIDER-MAN

You have courage, brains, and seek only justice, not fame. You are like Spider-Man – a true super-hero!

SUPER-VILLAIN < < < < < < < < > > > > > > > > **SUPER-HERO**